INTERCULTURAL DEVELOPMENT
IDRA
RESEARCH ASSO

NATIONAL BILINGUAL
MULTICULTURAL NETWORK
For Young Children   Region VI
5835 Callaghan Rd., Suite 350
San Antonio, Texas 78228

From Texas to Illinois

A FELIPE ADVENTURE STORY

From Texas to Illinois

Florance W. Taylor

Pictures by George Overlie

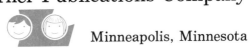

Lerner Publications Company

Minneapolis, Minnesota

With gratitude to the canning company officials involved, the local migrant council, and the public schools, especially to Mr. W.E. Schellhardt, Mr. N.E. Duchette, Mr. Leland Bergstrom, Mrs. Mary Messner, Mrs. Dorothy Whitehouse, and Mrs. Helen Kaufman.

International Standard Book Number: 0-8225-0141-4
Library of Congress Catalog Card Number: 79-165315

Second Printing 1973

To Alan Mack Taylor

Ten-year-old Felipe Fuentes walked through the dark streets beside his father. Felipe carried their big *frijole* kettle filled with cooking utensils. Papa had his guitar tucked under one arm, and he held little brother Luis in the other.

Mama walked behind them with the twins, Roberto and Juanito. The little boys were already sleepy, but they were only five years old. Mama carried all of the family's clothes—they had very few—tied up in a large black cloth.

The Fuentes were on their way to the truck stop to join a group of farm workers. Every spring they left their home in the Texas Rio Grande Valley and traveled to northern Texas. They went to pick cotton until autumn.

But this April it was different. They were going to work in a new, strange place—Illinois.

Papa had not known until suppertime that they would leave so soon. Their neighbor, Mr. Caranza, had knocked on their door and told them to be ready to board the truck at eleven o'clock that night. How they had hurried to get ready! Mama scrubbed and dressed the little boys and made Felipe take a bath. When he had put on clean clothes, she told him to catch their rooster and the four old hens. After quite a chase, he caught them all. Then he took them to Grandmother for safekeeping. Papa didn't do much except take his guitar from its place on the wall and get in Mama's way.

Papa hummed a happy tune as his family prepared to leave Texas. He looked forward to working in a new place and making more money than ever before. But Mama winked away a few tears. She did not want to leave Texas, because of the new baby that was coming. She wanted it to be born in Texas.

Felipe did not want to leave Texas either, and he was even more unhappy than Mama. Texas is our home, not Illinois, he thought, as he took some quick steps to catch up with his father. What will Illinois be like? Will we be happy there all summer? The more Felipe thought about it, the more unhappy he became.

He had not told Mama and Papa how he felt about leaving Texas. Felipe knew that they would make more money working in Illinois.

When the Fuentes reached the truck stop, many families were already waiting. The men were singing and strumming their guitars while the women talked in high-pitched, excited voices.

The workers were all Texans, but the grown-ups spoke only Spanish, the language of their Mexican ancestors. The children had learned English at school and used it when they talked to each other. At home they spoke Spanish with their parents.

Soon the Caranza family arrived. Carlos Caranza was a friend of Felipe's. He was two years older and had been in Illinois the summer before.

Papa Fuentes had not had time to tell his family much about their work in Illinois, so Felipe asked Carlos, "Do we pick cotton in Illinois?"

Carlos laughed. "You're sort of dumb, Felipe. They don't grow much cotton in Illinois. The grown-ups work on farms picking vegetables, like asparagus, sweet corn, and tomatoes."

"Do we get to work too?" asked Felipe.

"No," replied Carlos, "not during the school year. We have to go to school up there."

Felipe's face looked happier. "That suits me," he said. "I like to go to school."

Carlos frowned. "I don't. I'd rather work in the fields."

"I just hope we like it there," said Felipe.

After everyone had waited about half an hour, a big truck arrived. Big Pablo, the driver and crew leader, climbed down from his seat.

"We're ready to load," he shouted. "There's a seat for each of you in the truck." He pointed to the empty chairs in the truck bed. "Now, families get together. When I call your name, step forward." Big Pablo began reading from a list in his hand.

"Alvarez."

The five members of the Alvarez family moved toward the truck. Big Pablo pointed out their chairs. "Sit down and please be quiet," he said.

"Caranza. Fuentes," he called.

Just a few minutes after the Fuentes family was seated, Roberto, Juanito, and little Luis fell asleep. But Felipe was as wide awake as his parents.

At last Big Pablo said, "Now that all you migrants have a seat, let's go." Then he laughed heartily. "They call us migrants up north in Illinois. Don't ask me why, I don't know."

The truck began to roll along the highway. Some of the men strummed their guitars softly and the women sang. But soon the hum of the tires began to lull them to sleep.

Just before Felipe fell asleep, he looked out at the big starry Texas sky and said sadly, "*Hasta la vista*, sunny Texas, our home. *Hasta la vista*."

Felipe soon discovered that it was a long way to Illinois. They rode for several days, stopping only to stretch their legs and to eat. Usually they had good meals at the truck stops. On the last day of the trip it rained. The truck leaked, and everyone was damp and cold.

After an early supper they arrived at the town of Lockton, Illinois. The truck left the highway and entered a big open area next to a railroad track. It stopped between two big frame buildings.

Big Pablo jumped down from his high seat. He unfastened the tailgate at the back of the truck. "Everybody out," he cried. "Bring your belongings with you."

"It's cold," Mama said, when they were standing on the wet ground.

"It is cold," Felipe agreed, shivering in his thin cotton clothes. He looked around. They were in a large lot enclosed with a high wire fence. There were puddles of water everywhere, because of the rain.

This isn't at all like home, thought Felipe. Will we be cold like this all the time? But before he could ask anyone, he heard Big Pablo's voice.

"Follow me!" Big Pablo called, and he led the way into a long building.

The inside was larger than the gym of Felipe's Texas school. In the front part was a laundry, and Felipe saw several washers and dryers there.

The center of the building was filled with picnic tables and benches. Beside each big table was a smaller one which held a two-burner kerosene stove. Large electric refrigerators stood at each end of the room.

Everybody began talking about the stoves and refrigerators.

"Quiet!" Big Pablo shouted. "Now I'll explain. This room is for eating and cooking. Each family has one small and one large table, a stove, and space in one refrigerator. Mind you, don't quarrel over the food space."

He pointed to a row of doors over on the left side. "Those doors open into your sleeping rooms. Each family has one room. Choose one now and put your things in it. Then I'll show you more of the camp."

It was dark in the Fuentes' room. But Felipe soon found a light switch on the inside wall, and he flipped it quickly. A light bulb hanging from the ceiling lit up the room. Felipe set the big *frijole* kettle on the floor.

"Look, beds!" Papa said, pointing to some double bunks along the side walls.

"And a chest of drawers," cried Mama. She put the black sack of clothes on it.

Next Big Pablo took everyone outside to see the bath house. Large electric lights flooded the lot now, making the camp almost as bright as day.

In the bath house, Big Pablo said, "Plenty of showers and toilets here for all. Be sure you are clean whenever you leave this camp. That's an order. Now, any questions?"

"Do we work tomorrow?" asked one of the men.

"Sure," replied Big Pablo. "In the morning I'll give you a little money to buy groceries. You may pay some of it back to the company each pay day. Do your shopping early. At noon the company bus will take you to work in the fields."

He looked down at the children. "You'll go to school in Lockton tomorrow. Remember to work hard in school."

Then Big Pablo cried, "Okay, that's all."

Felipe felt more cheerful now. Illinois didn't seem so bad after all. Just then Carlos joined him. Felipe asked his friend, "Will it always be cold like this?"

Carlos laughed. "They have summer up here too, just like we do in Texas. Only it doesn't get as hot as Texas. And that's better for working in the fields."

Felipe looked up at a large factory building outlined against the dark sky.

"What's the name of that company?" he asked.

"The Midwest Canning Company," replied Carlos. "They ship canned vegetables all over the country."

"What is the name of the school we're going to? What is it like?" asked Felipe.

"Hey, you sure are full of questions," said Carlos, as they walked back to the building. "Anyway, you'll find out about all that tomorrow. See you then."

Felipe said good night to Carlos and went back to his family's room. Mama was putting their clothes into the drawers, and Papa had just finished hanging his guitar on the wall. Felipe sat down on a bunk next to him.

"I was sorry to leave Texas," Felipe began.

"I know," said Papa. "I could tell by your face. How do you feel now that we are finally here in Lockton?"

Felipe answered, "Well, I thought we were going away from our home. We had always lived in Texas. But now I think we just took our home with us. After all, our whole family is here, and so are our good friends. I guess we don't need anything else to feel at home."

"You have learned something important, Felipe," said Papa, smiling at his son. "And I'm sure this will be a good summer for all of us."

Felipe
Adventure Stories

From Texas to Illinois

What Is a Migrant?

Ball Two!

The School Picnic

Where's Luis?

The Corn Festival

A Plane Ride

We specialize in producing quality books for young people. For a complete list please write

Lerner Publications Company

241 First Avenue North, Minneapolis, Minnesota 55401